THE Arabian Nights
COLORING BOOK

by VIRGINIA FRANCES STERRETT

A collection of 1,001 adventurous and fanciful tales, the
Arabian Nights stories were told in Persia, Arabia, India,
and Asia for thousands of years before they were written
down. These ancient tales have been translated into
many languages and are still beloved throughout the
world. Maybe you've heard of the most famous tales:
*Aladdin and the Wonderful Lamp, The Seven Voyages
of Sindbad the Sailor,* and *Ali Baba and the Forty Thieves.*
The stories take place in far-off, exotic lands and are
full of action, intrigue, romance, comedy, and revenge.
Their main characters often find themselves in
remarkable and dangerous situations, which they
overcome by using magic or clever trickery.

The line drawings in this coloring book are based on
the elegant illustrations of Virginia Frances Sterrett; they
were created for an American edition of *The Arabian
Nights* published in 1928. Her original artworks are
reproduced on the inside front and back covers. When
you fill in the drawings, you might want to refer to
Sterrett's color schemes or you might choose different
ones. The last two pages of this book are blank so you
can create pictures of your own. Can you make
illustrations for your own magical tales?

Pomegranate kids®
AGES 3 to 103!

All works of art were created by Virginia Frances Sterrett for *The Arabian Nights,* edited by Hildegarde Hawthorne and published in 1928 by The Penn Publishing Company, a volume that is in the General Collections of the Library of Congress.

Pomegranate Communications, Inc.
Box 808022, Petaluma CA 94975
800 227 1428   www.pomegranate.com

Distributed by Pomegranate Europe Ltd.
Unit 1, Heathcote Business Centre, Hurlbutt Road
Warwick, Warwickshire CV34 6TD, UK
[+44] 0 1926 430111
sales@pomeurope.co.uk

Color reproductions © 2012 Library of Congress
Line drawings © Pomegranate Communications, Inc.
Catalog No. CB144
Cover design by Oky Sulistio, drawings rendered by Susan Koop
Printed in Korea

21 20 19 18 17 16 15 14 13 12   10 9 8 7 6 5 4 3 2 1

1. "The Sultana held conversation with a man."

2. "There appeared an old man leading a hind."

3. "'My son! My son!'"

4. "The Princess had great beauty."

5. "They supported him and carried him to the bottom."

6. "They danced before me with great skill."

7. "I opened the third door and found a large aviary."

8. "The serpent flew away."

9. "'Deliver me from this place.'"

10. "The genie disappeared immediately."

11. "The sultan and Aladdin ate by themselves."

12. "In this order they proceeded to the palace."

13. "Aladdin saluted her with joy."

14. "Presently a thick cloud arose."

15. "The robber disguised himself."

16. "Ali Baba examined all the jars."

17. "Morgiana danced with much grace."

18. "The sky became dark."

19. "We found it to be a gate of ebony."

20. "He carried me to a forest some leagues from town."

21. "Scheherazade went on with her story."

Draw and color your own picture here!

Draw and color your own picture here!